Legend of Land and Sky

Contents

Written by Jonny Walker

Illustrated by Martin Bustamante

Collins

Thousands of years ago, incredible tales were told to explain things that are tricky to understand.

These tales helped to explain why the sun shines.
They explained the noise of storms and
the quaking of the ground.

Sun and moon

Long ago in Denmark, the existence of the sun and moon were explained with this tale ...

A man boasted of his perfect children to the gods. The gods punished him for bragging.

From that instant, his children had to heave
the sun and moon across the sky ...

... for eternity!

In a story from Kenya, the sun and moon were bickering brothers.

While they scuffled, the moon fell into some runny mud.

This mud dimmed the moon's shine, explaining why the sun looks brighter than the moon.

Storm

Storms destroy the peace.

Old Icelandic tales describe thunder as the mighty thuds and deafening whacks of Thor's bulky hammer.

In tales from Greece, lightning bolts were the weapon of choice for the king of the gods.

He liked to throw them at his foes.

Quakes

Sometimes, the ground rumbles beneath our feet.

In Greece, they blamed these quakes on the Hundred-Handers. When these galumphing giants stomped, it made the ground shake.

In Japan, quakes were explained by the flailing of a giant catfish named Namazu.

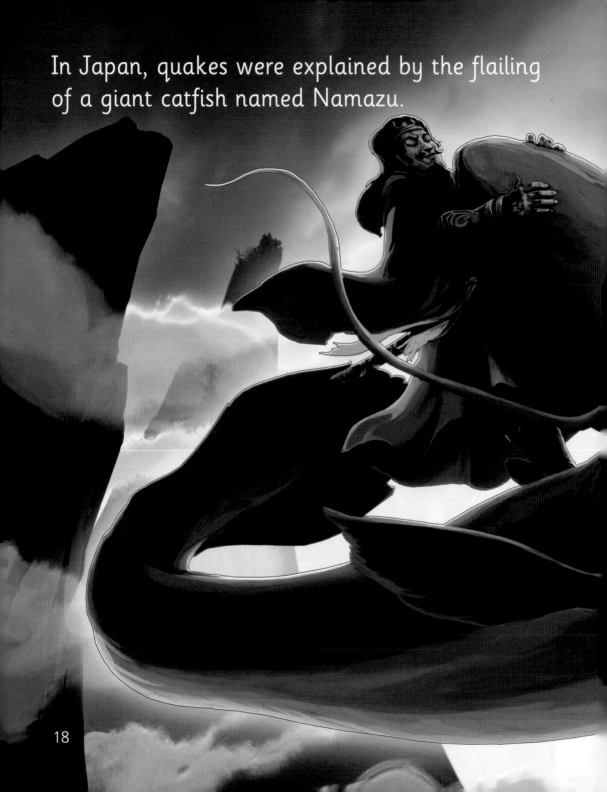

The thunder god placed a massive rock on Namazu's head to restrict him.

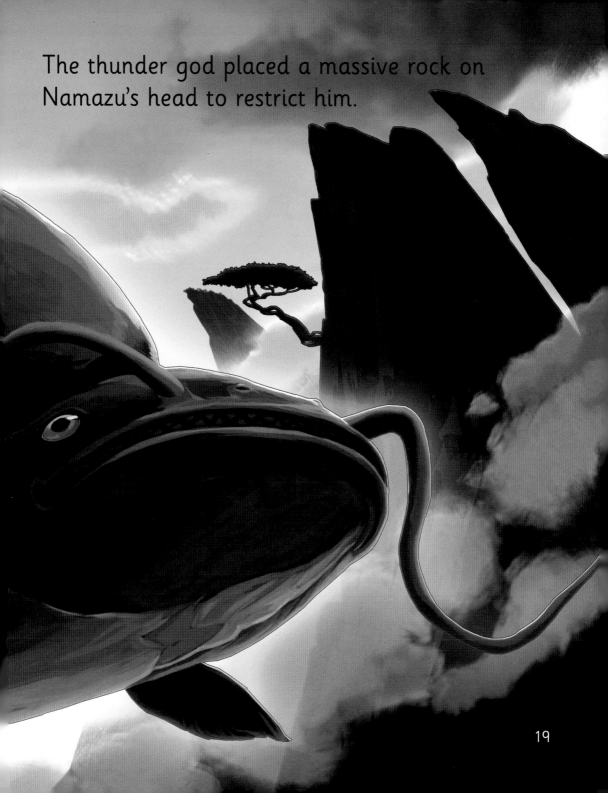

But Namazu thrashed his fins wildly!
When the rock tumbled off, it made quakes.

These old stories help us understand how people thought long ago.

The legends

Review: After reading

Use your assessment from hearing the children read to choose any GPCs, words or tricky words that need additional practice.

Read 1: Decoding

- Ask the children to read these words. Say: Look out for different ways of pronouncing the same grapheme.

  "ea": **heave   deafening**   "ow": **how   throw**

  "y" **mighty   why**   "g": **galumphing   giants**

- Encourage fluency by pointing to words randomly, and saying: Can you sound out these words silently in your head, before reading them aloud?

Read 2: Prosody

- Model choosing words to emphasise the meaning on page 13. Say: I'm going to emphasise the words that link with the massive noise of thunder. Point to: **mighty**, **deafening**, **bulky hammer**.
- Model reading page 14, then discuss with the children the important words on page 14 to emphasise (e.g. **lightning**, **weapon**, **king** – to link the thing being explained with the king and his weapon).

Read 3: Comprehension

- Ask the children to describe any legends they know. Ask: Does this legend try to explain something, too?
- Discuss why people had legends to explain things.
- Point to the word **boasted** on page 5. Discuss a definition. (*e.g. showed off, talked about how wonderful they were*)
  - Ask the children to check their definition works in the context of the page. Ask: What other word shows that he was showing off? (***bragging***)
- Ask children to work in pairs to retell one of the legends illustrated on pages 22 and 23. Encourage them to infer how people felt about the characters in the stories. Ask:
  - Do you think the gods in the legends were seen as cruel or fair? Why?
  - What were the main characteristics of Thor? Do you think people were afraid of him? Why?

He liked to throw them at his foes.

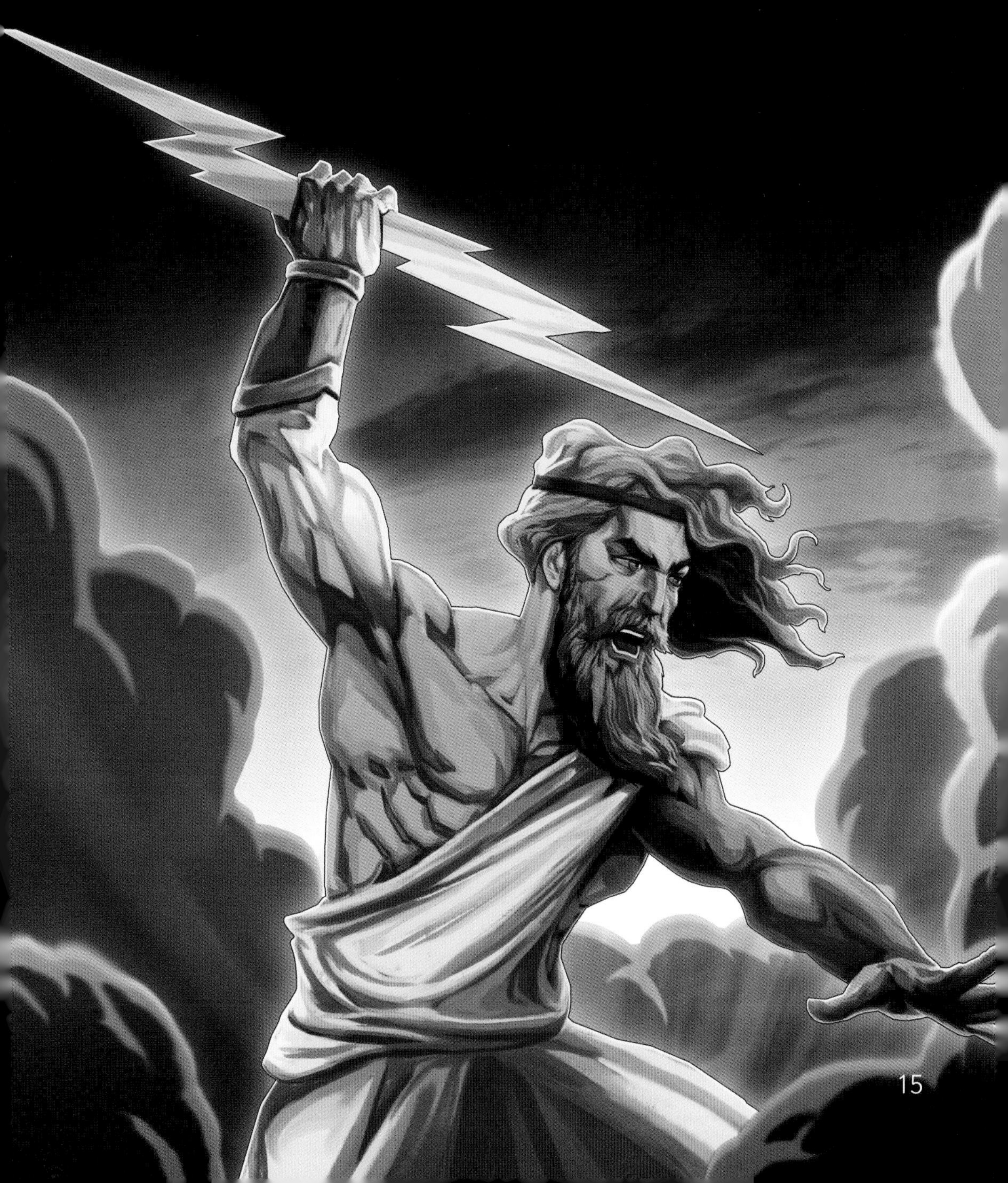